The
Margaret
Wise Brown
Treasury

PaRragon

Bath • New York • Singapore • Hong Kong • Cologne • Delhi
Melbourne • Amsterdam • Johannesburg • Shenzhen

This edition published by Parragon Inc. in 2013

Parragon Inc.
440 Park Avenue South, 13th Floor
New York, NY 10016
www.parragon.com

Written by Margaret Wise Brown
Cover typography by Emily Dove Gross
Edited by Lily Holland
Production by Joanne Knowlson

ISBN 978-1-4723-2339-2

Printed in China

Contents

Count to 10 with a mouse

to

with a

Illustrated by Kirsten Richards

There was a little

mouse

no bigger
than a
mole,

6

who lived in a **round** place
that he called a **hol**e.

He said,
"I'd better
learn to
count,"
and so the story goes.

1 mouse

One mouse, took one

8

look,
at
one
book,
that had one hole
to run through.

9

2 holes

Then the mouse ran through the book,

the mouse ran through the book.

He ran onto the neXt page,

to
take a
little
look.

3 fish

And there, what does he see?
And there, what does he see?

Three little fishes

12

Swimming in the sea.

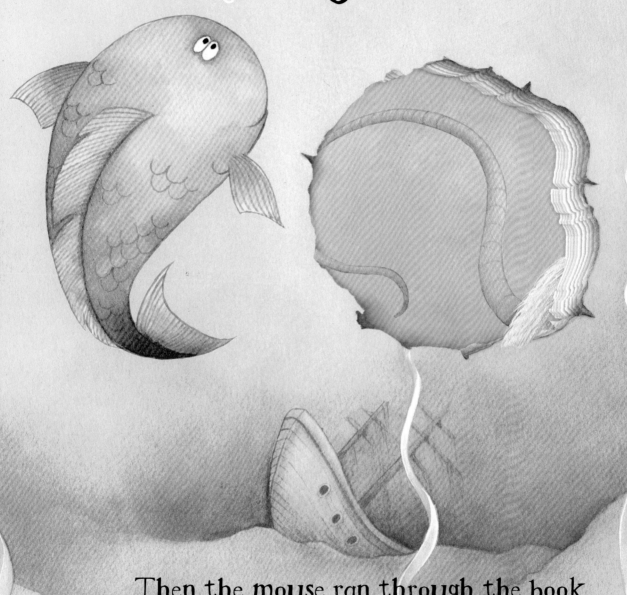

Then the mouse ran through the book,
the mouse ran through the book.
He ran onto the next page
to take a little look.

4 monkeys

And there, what does he see?
And there, what does he see?

Four little monkeys

Swinging in a tree.

Then the mouse ran through the book,
the mouse ran through the book.
He ran onto the next page
to take a little look.

5 butterflies

And here, great sakes alive!
And here, great sakes alive!

Here he found five butterflies,
one, two, three, four, five.

Then the mouse ran through the book,
the mouse ran through the book.
He ran onto the next page
to take a little look.

6 pussycats

And in among the mix ...
and in among the mix ...

siX little pussycats

are all in a fix.

So the mouse ran through the book,
the mouse ran through the book.
He ran onto the next page
to take a little look.

7 apples

And there, what does he see?
And there, what does he see?

seven little apples

upon an apple tree.

Then the mouse ran through the book,
the mouse ran through the book.
He ran onto the next page
to take a little look.

8 crows

And here is what he saw.
And here is what he saw.

caw!

Eight shiny black crows

caw!

caw!

learning how to caw.

caw!

w!

Then the mouse ran through the book,
the mouse ran through the book.
He ran onto the next page
to take a little look.

9 o'clock

Here everything is fine
The clock has just struck nine.
Nine o'clock is nine o'clock
and everything is fine.

O Hickory Dickory Dock,

the mouse ran **up** the clock.

Then Dockery Hickory Dock,
the Mouse ran **down** the clock.

Then the mouse ran through the book,
the mouse ran through the book.
He ran onto the next page
to take a little look.

1 2 3 4 5

And when he got to ten ...

and when he got to ten ...

6 7 8 9 10

he turned

around

the other way

and ran right back again.

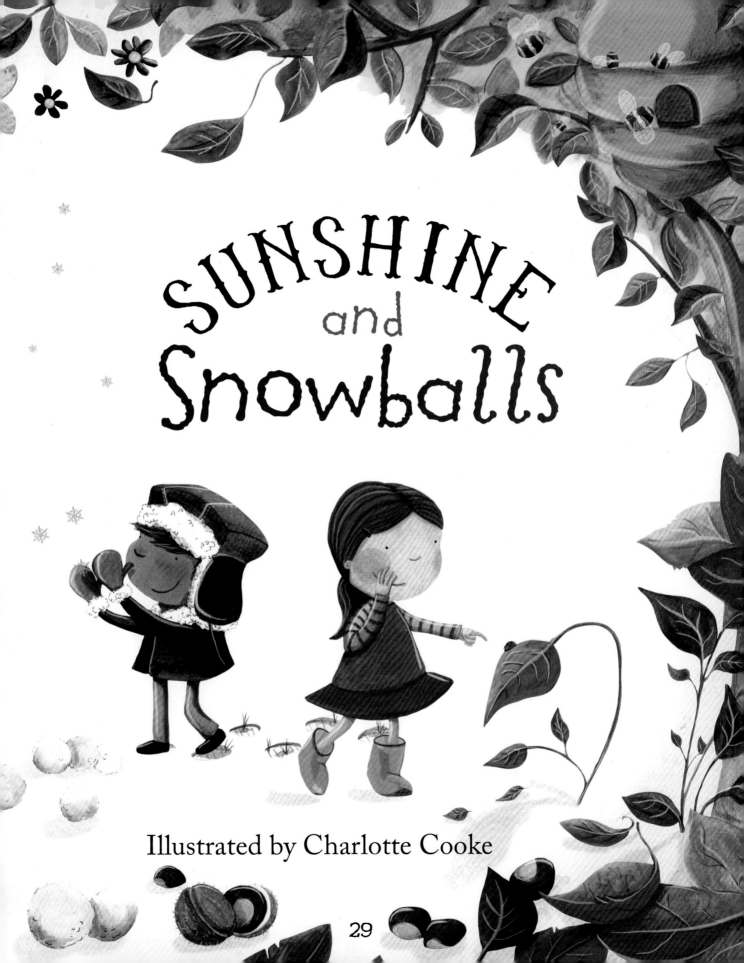

SUNSHINE and Snowballs

Illustrated by Charlotte Cooke

Summer, summer in the sun,

Flowers grow and bunnies run.

Snowballs, snowballs in the snow,

Snowflakes fall and cold winds blow.

Pussy willows in the spring,

Violets bloom and birds sing.

The wind blows hard across the hills,

And shakes the yellow daffodils.

The fog comes on without a sound,

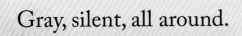

Gray, silent, all around.

Rain, rain on the windowpane,

Splashes once,

then splashes again.

Jagged lightning
    splits the sky,

Thunder rumbles, wild winds cry!

43

Orange pumpkins, yellow corn,

Purple grapes, and a frosty morn.

Smoke is drifting all around,

From raked leaves
on the ground.

47

Walk across the icy snow,

Footprints follow wherever you go.

Starlight, starlight, frosty bright,

Fills the spaces of the night.

Sleep Little Angel

Illustrated by Stephen Gulbis

Sleep little angel,
And never you cry.
Spring will come,
And spring will pass by.

I will sing of the violet,
Lest you forget,
Lest you forget,
My little one, the spring.

Sleep little angel,
The buzzing fly
Will soar in the summer that passes by.
Summer is here all wild and green,
And I will sing of the flowering bean.

I will sing of the firefly,
Lest you forget,
Lest you forget,
The summer that is not ended yet.

Sleep little angel,
This frosty night,
Fall has come,
Birds take their flight.

But I will sing of this same cold air,
The smell of chrysanthemums everywhere.

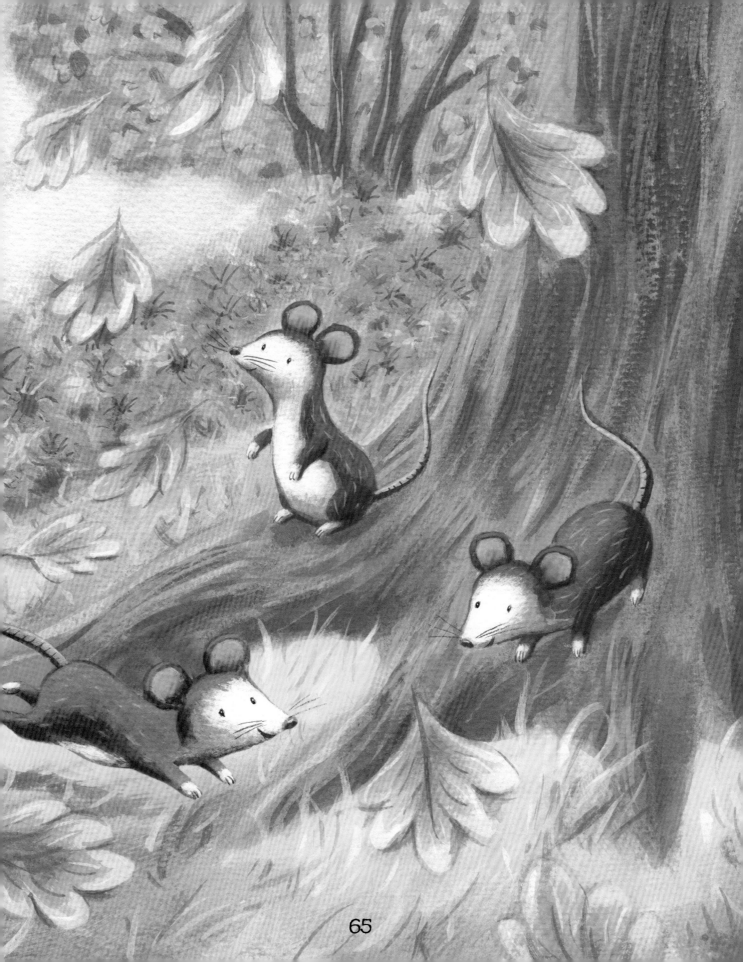

I will sing of the falling leaves,
Lest you forget,
Lest you forget,
The fall of the year is not ended yet.

Sleep little angel,
The sun goes down,
The snow is white on the frozen ground.

The snow is soft, and softly I'll sing
Of stars and every quiet thing.

I will sing of tall black trees that fret,
Lest you forget,
Lest you forget,
The ice and snow are not melted yet.

Sleep little angel, and I will sing
Of summer and winter and fall and spring,
Of stars and every quiet thing,
Of frost and primroses I will sing.

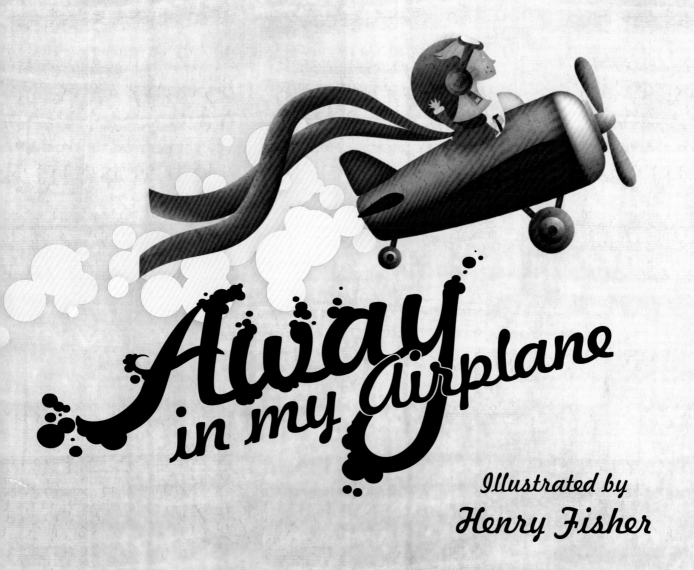

Away
in my Airplane

Illustrated by

Henry Fisher

Riding along in my

airplane,

Over the clouds

and through the rain.

Riding along in my airplane,

Sometimes I meet a bird way up high in the sky,

Flying almost as fast as I fly—

But not as high!

Riding along
in my airplane,

Out of the sunlight and

Then out of the clouds

and sun again,

Riding along in my airplane!

Down below the people go,

very small and very slow.

They look like bugs and ants and flies—
I wonder if they realize
What they look like to my eyes.

Riding along in my airplane,
I **wave** to the sun,

I shout to the rain.

Then, with a roar
of my motors
that drowns me out,

VROOM!

I dash straight up in the air
And wheel about.

I plunge through the sunlight,

I hurl through the rain,

Then I glide

down to the earth

in my airplane.

Hello!

Around the World We Go!

Illustrated by Christine Tappin

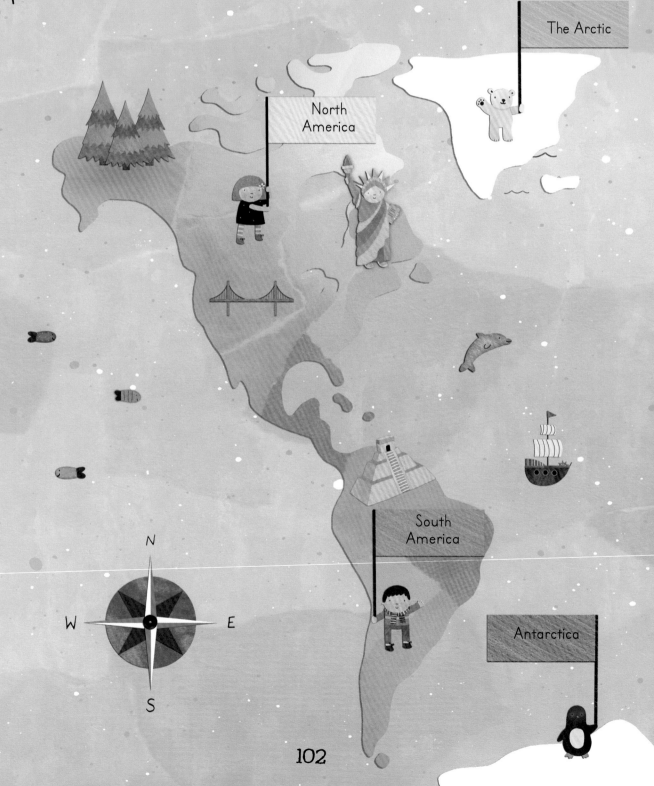

Around the world we go,

The Arctic

North America

South America

Antarctica

N
W   E
S

Europe

Asia

Africa

Australia

To learn what we don't know.

In foreign lands,
We'll all
shake
hands,

As around
the world we go!

Around the
world we go,

106

To learn what we don't know.

We'll make our eyes
A great big size

To see
what we
don't know.

Around the world we go,

Each language we don't know.

say "how do you do?"

Come
stai?

Aap kaise
hain?

As around the world we go.

113

Around the world we go,

In singing we can show

A way to play

In a friendly way,

As around the world we go.

Around the world we go,

The world is rather slow.

Because we run

ahead of the world,

As around we

the world
go!

Sleep Tight,
Sleepy Bears

Illustrated by
Julie Clay

There was a **big** sleepy bear,

and a little sleepy bear.

The big sleepy bear yawned

a great big yawn,

and the little sleepy
bear yawned
a little sleepy yawn.

Then the great
big bear

gave a great big

s t r e t c h,

and the little sleepy bear gave a little sleepy

s t r e t c h.

Then the **big** sleepy bear got into bed,

and the little sleepy bear got into bed.

133

Then the big sleepy bear sang

a sleepy song:

When I lay me down

to sleep,

Four bright angels

around me keep.

Two to watch me through the **night,**

And two
to **wake**
me come
daylight.

And the little sleepy bear sang

a sleepy song:

When I lay me down

to sleep,

Four bright angels

around me keep.

Two to watch me through the **night**,

And two to **wake** me come **daylight**.

Softer
and
softer
and
softer.

Then the **big** sleepy bear closed his eyes,

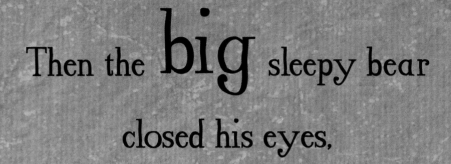

and the little sleepy bear closed his eyes.

And the little sleepy bear thought of the darkness, and the starlight,

142

and the **big** round moon,

and how he'd be sleeping soon.

Then the **big** sleepy bear whispered, "Sleep tight."

144

And the little sleepy
bear didn't say
a word because he
was sound asleep.

145

ALL THE
FAMILIES

Illustrated by Gabriel Alborozo

Everyone has a family.

Bunnies
have families.

See the
bunny family with
the nine baby
bunnies.

Dogs have families.

See the dog family
with the five baby
puppies.

153

Elephants have families.
See the elephant family with
one baby elephant.

And so have you a family.
Who is the baby?

When it is lunchtime,
and families get hungry,

156

really hungry,

what do they eat?

The bunny family with
the nine baby bunnies
nibble lettuce.

The dog family with
the five baby puppies
chew five bones.

The elephant family
with the one baby elephant
eat treetop buds.

All the families eat their food,
so YOU eat your food.

When it is nighttime
in the houses,
and in the rooms,
and out of the windows,

when it is really night,
what do the families do then?

The families go to sleep.

The bunny family with the nine baby bunnies
twitch their noses and fall asleep.

The dog family with the five baby puppies
curl up in balls and fall asleep.

The elephant family with the one baby elephant
hang down their ears and go to sleep.

All the families
go to sleep, and YOU
go to sleep.

Goodnight
Little One

Illustrated by Rebecca Elliott

Little donkey on the hill,
Standing there so very still.

Making faces at the skies,

Little donkey
close your eyes.

Little monkey in the tree,
Swinging there so merrily.
Throwing coconuts at the skies,

Little monkey
close *your* eyes.

181

Silly sheep that slowly crop,
Night has come and you must stop.

Chewing grass beneath the skies,
Silly sheep now close *your* eyes.

Wild young birds that sweetly sing,
Curve your heads beneath your wing.
Dark night covers all the skies,
Wild young birds now close your eyes.

Old black cat down in the barn,
Keeping five small kittens warm.
Let the wind blow in the skies,

Dear old black cat
close *your* eyes.

Little child all tucked in bed,
Looking such a sleepyhead.
Stars are quiet in the skies,

Little child now
close *your* eyes.